Success

10 Minute Tests

English

age 10 –11 · level four

Nick Barber

Sample page

clear instructional text

topic being covered

test number for quick reference

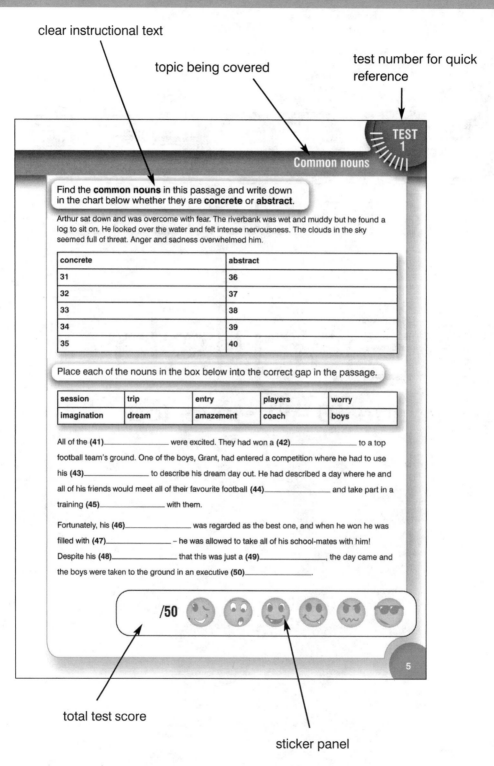

TEST 1

Common nouns

Find the **common nouns** in this passage and write down in the chart below whether they are **concrete** or **abstract**.

Arthur sat down and was overcome with fear. The riverbank was wet and muddy but he found a log to sit on. He looked over the water and felt intense nervousness. The clouds in the sky seemed full of threat. Anger and sadness overwhelmed him.

concrete	abstract
31	36
32	37
33	38
34	39
35	40

Place each of the nouns in the box below into the correct gap in the passage.

session	trip	entry	players	worry
imagination	dream	amazement	coach	boys

All of the (41)_____ were excited. They had won a (42)_____ to a top football team's ground. One of the boys, Grant, had entered a competition where he had to use his (43)_____ to describe his dream day out. He had described a day where he and all of his friends would meet all of their favourite football (44)_____ and take part in a training (45)_____ with them.

Fortunately, his (46)_____ was regarded as the best one, and when he won he was filled with (47)_____ – he was allowed to take all of his school-mates with him! Despite his (48)_____ that this was just a (49)_____, the day came and the boys were taken to the ground in an executive (50)_____.

/50

5

total test score

sticker panel

2

Contents

Underline the **common nouns** in these sentences.
There may be more than one in a sentence.

1. The boy sat down.
2. Every girl wore make-up.
3. None of the bands were any good.
4. The river burst its banks and flooded the town.
5. Tara scrubbed her feet.
6. Rain fell on Tom's umbrella.
7. The puppy bit the chair.
8. Canoes are used to travel on rivers.
9. The desk collapsed when Fred sat on it.
10. All the answers from the class were the same.
11. Cars and trains were used by the girls.
12. The hat did not fit.
13. Soldiers marched past the monument.
14. Lisa's goldfish was orange.
15. Every boy ate his sandwiches.

Circle the **common abstract** nouns in these sentences.
There may be more than one in a sentence.

Example: (Joy) filled their faces.

16. The day ended.
17. Robbie was filled with happiness.
18. The girls showed great intelligence when they did the test.
19. The football supporters were suffering from extreme boredom.
20. Bravery is a good quality to have.
21. The woman's kindness affected everybody greatly.
22. There was no love lost between the boxers.
23. It took great courage for Denise to jump out of the aeroplane.
24. Wilf felt great joy when he scored.
25. "Your imagination will cause you fear," said Dawn.
26. Beauty is only skin deep.
27. Revenge was not necessary for the boxer.
28. Please help people suffering with loneliness.
29. The workers were rewarded for their loyalty.
30. The juggler demonstrated great skill.

Find the **common nouns** in this passage and write down in the chart below whether they are **concrete** or **abstract**.

Arthur sat down and was overcome with fear. The riverbank was wet and muddy but he found a log to sit on. He looked over the water and felt intense nervousness. The clouds in the sky seemed full of threat. Anger and sadness overwhelmed him.

concrete	abstract
31	36
32	37
33	38
34	39
35	40

Place each of the nouns in the box below into the correct gap in the passage.

session	trip	entry	players	worry
imagination	dream	amazement	coach	boys

All of the **(41)**_____ were excited. They had won a **(42)**_____ to a top

football team's ground. One of the boys, Grant, had entered a competition where he had to use

his **(43)**_____ to describe his dream day out. He had described a day where he and

all of his friends would meet all of their favourite football **(44)**_____ and take part in a

training **(45)**_____ with them.

Fortunately, his **(46)**_____ was regarded as the best one, and when he won he was

filled with **(47)**_____ – he was allowed to take all of his school-mates with him!

Despite his **(48)**_____ that this was just a **(49)**_____, the day came and

the boys were taken to the ground in an executive **(50)**_____.

/50

In the passage below are ten proper nouns.
Write them in the boxes after the passage.

Last summer I went on holiday to Colorado in the United States. I stayed in a town called Estes Park, which is on the border of the Rocky Mountain National Park. After staying there for a week and attending a festival in a town called Lyons, I drove to Denver and caught a flight to Louisiana. My holiday was cut short because Hurricane Gustav meant that all tourists had to leave. Back home in England, I said to myself, "Nick, you're a lucky man!"

1	2	3	4	5
6	7	8	9	10

Look at this list. For each one, tick whether it is a proper noun, a common noun, or not a noun.

word	common noun	proper noun	not a noun
11. Arthur			
12. college			
13. stupid			
14. Edinburgh			
15. guitar			
16. George			
17. motorway			
18. random			
19. Andy			
20. several			

Fill in this chart with proper nouns starting with each letter of the alphabet – there are lots of different answers that you might give for this. The first one has been done for you.

letter	place name	first name
A	Australia	Amy
21. B		
22. C		
23. D		
24. E		
25. F		
26. G		
27. H		
28. I		
29. J		
30. K		
31. L		
32. M		
33. N		
34. O		
35. P		
36. Q		
37. R		
38. S		
39. T		
40. U		
41. V		
42. W		
43. X		
44. Y		
45. Z		

/45

Write down the plural form of each of these words.

1. girl _____
2. church _____
3. age _____
4. exam _____
5. bully _____
6. wife _____
7. lens _____
8. tax _____
9. loss _____
10. fairy _____
11. elf _____
12. sandwich _____
13. loaf _____
14. tooth _____
15. army _____
16. sheep _____
17. man _____
18. thief _____
19. self _____
20. batch _____

In this passage, change all of the underlined words into plurals, so that the passage make sense!

The girl (21)_____ went for a ride on their pony (22)_____, as it was a sunny day. As they rode along, they noticed the chimney (23)_____ on a nearby farm had been blown down in last night's storm. They weren't the only witness (24)_____ to what had happened. Some person (25)_____ who had been out camping had noticed it too. The riders said to themself (26)_____ that they were lucky to live in such sturdy house (27)_____ .

The girls continued their ride and noticed someone selling strawberry (28)_____ by the side of the road. They dismounted and started telling each other story (29)_____, until a few of the girls noticed that the fruit had attracted some mosquito (30)_____ and they'd all been bitten!

All of the following nouns have irregular plurals – but what are they?

31. analysis _____
32. stimulus _____

33. axis _____
34. crisis _____

35. ox _____
36. oasis _____

37. woman _____
38. medium _____

39. deer _____
40. louse _____

41. child _____
42. cactus _____

43. fish _____
44. species _____

45. goose _____
46. moose _____

47. offspring _____
48. emphasis _____

49. scissors _____
50. mouse _____

51–60. Here are ten plural words. Create a story, which makes sense, using all of them, in the space below. There are lots of possible ways that you might do this and you do not have to use them in any order.

> dogs cats owners houses streets habits pets complaints gardens

_____

_____

_____

_____

_____

_____

/60

In each of these sentences, change the underlined word for the correct pronoun.

1. **Robert** married Tara.   _____

2. Robert married **Tara.**   _____

3. **My sister and I** went shopping.   _____

4. Michelle brought **her present.**   _____

5. **Emma** has got a twin sister.   _____

6. **The goldfish** was swimming.   _____

7. **Laura** had long hair.   _____

8. Josh spoke to **the boys.**   _____

9. Joe joined **the band.**   _____

10. **The band** hired Joe as their singer. _____

Read this passage and circle the correct pronouns from the choices given.

Zak the pop star wanted his assistant, Lucy, to get **(11) him/her/them** a new microphone for his

act. The last microphone he had used wasn't very good because **(12) he/she/it** had broken

within five minutes of the start of his concert. **(13) She/He/They** had warned Zak that buying

cheap microphones was not a good idea because of this very problem. Lucy was rather fed up of

telling **(14) him/her/them** about such things and, in fact, she was considering getting a new job.

(15) She/He/They had worked together since the early part of Zak's career, but now **(16)**

she/he/they felt that it was time to move on and get a fresh start. Zak wasn't aware of Lucy's feel-

ings and still treated **(17) her/him/them** as though there were no problems. **(18) She/He/They**

went and bought a new microphone and tested **(19) it/him/her** before she handed it over to **(20)**

him/her/them.

In each of these sentences, tick the correct pronoun for the underlined words.

21. The professor never gives **the students** homework.

     a) me ☐   **b)** them ☐   **c)** you ☐

22. I gave the book to **my little niece.**

     a) her ☐   **b)** us ☐   **c)** him ☐

23. The boys are playing with **their console games.**

     a) it ☐   **b)** them ☐   **c)** her ☐

24. My mother is sending a gift to **Robbie.**

     a) me ☐   **b)** her ☐   **c)** him ☐

25. I guessed **the answer.**

     a) she ☐   **b)** her ☐   **c)** it ☐

26. Mia is going to see **Becky.**

     a) her ☐   **b)** him ☐   **c)** me ☐

27. Shut **the door**, please.

     a) it ☐   **b)** them ☐   **c)** us ☐

28. Can you tell **the people** the way to Port Vale's ground?

     a) you ☐   **b)** them ☐   **c)** us ☐

29. The gifts are for **Claire.**

     a) him ☐   **b)** her ☐   **c)** you ☐

30. Can you give directions to **my wife and me**?

     a) her ☐   **b)** me ☐   **c)** us ☐

/30

In each sentence, circle the verb which makes the most sense.

Example: Stuart played/ate/chose his bass guitar very well.

Answer: Stuart **played** his bass guitar very well.

1. Paul ran/scoffed/ate all the way to the shops to get there before they closed.

2. Phil didn't realise/fry/torment how much money he'd made.

3. Eating/squinting/locating jelly was not an option because of her special diet.

4. Jessica started to tweak/shake/scribble with fear.

5. The referee disguised/digested/spoiled the game for the fans.

6. Barney did not cough/speak/loan to his friends all night.

7. "Don't dribble/squeak/eat peas with a spoon!" said Ellie.

8. Lucie frowned/gargled/smiled with happiness.

9. The light exploded/lit/smothered when the fuse box broke.

10. Joanne smoked/waited/shouted loudly across the room.

Choose an appropriate verb to complete each sentence. There are lots of different possible answers.

11. Chris _____ the drums.

12. Craig _____ off his chair.

13. Nick _____ presents for his nieces.

14. Irene _____ until dinner time and then woke up.

15. Ellie _____ away because she didn't like photographs.

16. Dave's camera had been _____ from his car.

17. Peter's kitchen was _____ to make it look as good as new.

18. Sylvia _____ what time it was because she'd lost her watch.

19. Arthur _____ a new part for the broken clock all by himself.

20. Lucie's painting _____ in the exhibition.

Look at the words in the table. Tick to show whether each one is a verb, a noun, both or neither. The first one is done for you.

Word	Just a Verb	Just a Noun	Both	Neither
talking			✔	
21. silliness				
22. run				
23. joke				
24. cry				
25. document				
26. fear				
27. show				
28. table				
29. sympathy				
30. happy				
31. questioning				
32. talk				
33. decommission				
34. pretty				
35. clever				
36. blissful				
37. smell				
38. awkwardly				
39. study				
40. dump				

/40

Verb-subject agreement

In these sentences, circle the correct form of the verb so that each one makes sense.

1. Donna **was running/were running** the party.

2. Donna and Tracy **was organising/were organising** the reception.

3. Brenton **is coming/are coming** to the match.

4. Sean and David **is going/are going** to the cinema.

5. Mike and Neil **are/is** neighbours.

6. Scientists **are working/is working** on a cure for the common cold.

7. Noise **was/were** a problem for people living next to the main road.

8. The results **is/are** final.

9. Why did the others ask if they **was/were** coming along?

10. Marie **is getting/are getting** ready for the meal.

Tick whether these sentences have the correct form of verb and subject agreement. The first one is done for you as an example.

Sentence	Correct Verb-Subject	Incorrect Verb-Subject
The boys **are** playing football tonight.	✔	
11. Hermione and her friends is going out.		
12. Emma is changing her job.		
13. Nobody knew what Lisa were doing.		
14. Tara and Mark are going to Leeds.		
15. Lanchester United was a made up name for a football team.		
16. What was they thinking of?		
17. Hannah weren't happy.		
18. Kathryn and Tom were cleaning.		
19. Nobody knew that Helena were a secret agent!		
20. James was getting ready.		

Verb-subject agreement

Complete these sentences with the correct
form of the verb, using: **is**, **are**, **was** or **were**.

Example: Marie _____ working last week but not next week.

Answer: Marie **was** working last week, but not next week.

21. James _____ going to see Michelle next week.

22. Michelle and Emma _____ staying at their mum's house when the power cut happened.

23. Andrew _____ taking pictures of the holiday when he dropped his camera.

24. Courtney _____ finishing her essay when the teacher said that the exam time was up.

25. Rodney _____ going on holiday soon.

26. Kurt _____ living in Kentucky, at this moment in time.

27. Nobody knew if Dorothy _____ telling the truth about her lottery win.

28. Johanna _____ baking gingerbread men for tonight's meal.

29. Ed _____ looking for his keys yesterday.

30. Richard _____ getting ready to perform at this very moment.

31–40. Write some sentences, using each of the words in Q21 to 30. There are lots of different
answers that you might give.

_____

_____

_____

_____

_____

/40

Past tense

Change these sentences into the past tense by changing each highlighted word for a past tense single word verb.

1. Mia **eats** broccoli. _____

2. Eleanna **performs** in amateur dramatics. _____

3. Alan **stands** outside the school gates. _____

4. Samantha **rides** her horse. _____

5. Alexandra **has** long hair. _____

6. Kellie **giggles.** _____

7. Robbie **sings** to himself, quietly. _____

8. Mark **invents** things. _____

9. Alicia **sits** in silence. _____

10. Tom **knits** socks for babies. _____

Complete this table, using the different forms of the past tense. An example has been done for you.

Verb	Past Perfect Tense	Simple Past Tense
arrive	I have arrived	I arrived
11. find		
12. study		
13. teach		
14. do		
15. call		
16. shout		
17. catch		
18. clap		
19. bring		
20. go		

Change these sentences from their current tense into
the past tense, **changing as few words as possible.**

Example: Marie **is** eating fish and chewing vegetables at the same time.

Answer: Marie **was** eating fish and chewing vegetables at the same time.

21. The football team are losing at half time.

_____

22. Chuck sings and plays guitar in a band.

_____

23. Catherine buys strange clothes.

_____

24. Liam wears fancy dress costumes at parties.

_____

25. Laura rarely asks questions.

_____

26. Isaac smiles a lot, especially when he concentrates.

_____

27. Whitney's loud voice fills the room.

_____

28. Ari walks into the classroom when she is ready.

_____

29. Samuel invests in internet based companies.

_____

30. Maisie enjoys school holidays because she can lie in.

_____

/30

Circle the adjectives in these sentences.

1. The dull, dreary day carried on as it had started.

2. Happy people work hard.

3. Exciting football matches happen frequently.

4. The cute hamsters ate their food.

5. Henry walked past the tall, imposing gate.

6. Faye's jewellery was expensive.

7. Loud shouts were heard from the playground.

8. The skilful forward raced past the defender.

9. There were no more fashionable shoes left in the sale.

10. Todd sang his humorous songs.

Place adjectives in the following sentences. There are lots of different answers.

11. The _____ girl sang very well.

12. After the _____ party, everyone had to tidy up.

13. Before the _____ meeting, Don sorted out his notes.

14. Before the meeting, Don had to sort out his _____ notes.

15. Every game was as _____ as the first one.

16. Lucie's _____ uncle bought her presents for her birthday.

17. Ellie disliked eating _____ cabbage.

18. Chuck walked from his _____ house to the shops.

19. Abraham enjoyed taking photos with his _____ camera.

20. Lisa watched the _____ weather from her window.

Place adjectives in this passage to make it sound mysterious and spooky. There are lots of different answers, but all of the adjectives you choose should help to build up the right kind of mood.

The **(21)** _____ man walked through the **(22)** _____ gate and saw the

(23) _____ house. He walked through the **(24)** _____ garden and

approached the **(25)** _____ door. The house looked **(26)** _____ and

(27) _____ , but he knocked on the door anyway. After a few **(28)** _____

moments the door opened and a **(29)** _____ figure stood in front of him. The man

walked into the **(30)** _____ hallway.

Now complete the passage again, but this time choose adjectives that will make the passage sound light-hearted and jolly.

The **(31)** _____ man walked through the **(32)** _____ gate and saw the

(33) _____ house. He walked through the **(34)** _____ garden and

approached the **(35)** _____ door. The house looked **(36)** _____ and

(37) _____, but he knocked on the door anyway. After a few **(38)** _____

moments the door opened and a **(39)** _____ figure stood in front of him. The man

walked into the **(40)** _____ hallway.

Complete the passage again, this time choosing adjectives that will make it sound like an action adventure.

The **(41)** _____ man walked through the **(42)** _____ gate and saw the

(43) _____ house. He walked through the **(44)** _____ garden and

approached the **(45)** _____ door. The house looked **(46)** _____ and

(47) _____, but he knocked on the door anyway. After a few **(48)** _____

moments the door opened and a **(49)** _____ figure stood in front of him. The man

walked into the **(50)** _____ hallway.

/50

Below is a list of verbs – find them in the grid. They may be found backwards, forwards, up, down or diagonally in any direction.

A	C	K	E	N	C	O	U	R	A	G	E	F	X	E	P	K	P	Q	C
P	H	R	Q	G	T	G	C	H	K	F	X	I	E	G	N	X	T	B	V
V	L	U	M	S	U	D	I	O	D	N	H	N	Q	M	E	T	L	T	L
N	J	K	R	X	L	T	V	W	C	K	J	I	U	W	W	X	T	M	V
U	T	O	R	P	W	S	N	Q	H	R	J	S	A	V	U	X	R	E	B
M	F	J	O	A	A	R	W	K	W	N	E	H	F	G	O	K	S	O	I
B	Z	G	B	W	C	B	B	A	F	H	S	A	I	R	Y	K	O	E	C
I	D	Y	P	P	H	E	T	K	N	A	I	N	T	U	N	V	X	H	I
U	E	B	U	M	Z	M	W	Y	C	Z	M	S	W	E	I	I	P	R	S
R	U	N	V	J	I	J	I	I	F	I	T	I	T	K	L	A	T	S	B
K	F	B	W	M	W	P	N	V	D	N	K	G	H	L	N	L	O	R	W
U	V	U	V	D	G	M	X	N	L	G	A	H	F	B	E	R	L	P	V
S	F	I	N	D	W	D	E	E	D	D	T	L	L	G	C	O	W	U	G
R	L	C	Q	M	R	R	Y	A	P	Y	L	K	T	W	X	R	Y	F	K
E	A	H	W	U	O	R	A	O	A	T	A	E	B	A	C	X	A	S	J
D	F	E	H	C	E	I	J	Y	R	S	P	P	K	T	Q	X	J	F	J
N	L	E	S	P	U	W	B	X	T	D	B	A	Y	O	P	W	G	J	Y
A	Y	R	O	F	J	O	F	G	U	Y	G	N	L	R	I	E	T	N	P
W	T	A	C	K	L	E	K	D	E	S	O	L	E	F	I	H	S	F	G
P	T	I	N	J	U	R	E	G	X	W	S	P	M	L	B	J	A	K	Q

RUN	CREATE	FINISH
TALK	KICK	FLY
WANDER	WHISTLE	FLAP
SCORE	CHEER	TRAP
RACE	TACKLE	ENCOURAGE
WIN	LOSE	CROSS
INJURE	BEAT	

Complete the crossword below by using the clues. All of the answers are adjectives.

Across

2. Twitchy and a bit scared
4. Huge
7. Not noisy
13. In a good mood
14. Not wanting to do something
16. Unusual, often in a good way
18. Not hot
19. Pretty, or attractive
20. Frightened

Down

1. In a bad mood
3. Not rough
5. Dull and overcast
6. Not dull
8. Hard to believe; amazing
9. Not very nice
10. Almost too small to be seen
11. Unable to be achieved
12. Not soft
15. Intelligent
17. Hurt

Adverbs

In these sentences, there is an adjective in brackets. Change it into an adverb, so that the sentence will make sense.

1.   The athlete ran _____ (quick) to the finish line.

2.   Robbie _____ (amazing) released 50 songs on his new album.

3.   Tara smiled _____ (reluctant) when she saw that she had to eat the carrots.

4.   Dev ambled _____ (lazy) to the shed.

5.   _____ (Astonishing), Jennifer had done her homework.

6.   _____ (Lucky), Danny had put the chicken in the oven on time.

7.   Kristina had _____ (fortunate) won the lottery.

8.   Peter had _____ (clever) found a way to solve the puzzle.

9.   The snow in June had _____ (crazy) forced the cricket match to be cancelled.

10. Katrina walked _____ (cautious) to the shops.

Not all words that end in **ly** are adverbs. Read these sentences and tick whether the word ending in **ly** is an adverb or an adjective.

Sentence	Adverb	Adjective
11. The **holy** man spoke well.		
12. Ray **nervously** ate the food.		
13. **Ugly** creatures are scary.		
14. **Smelly** streets need cleaning.		
15. **Carefully**, Sam packed her bags.		
16. Caesar **triumphantly** entered Rome.		
17. The teacher's **kindly** ways made him popular.		
18. Emma disliked walking in the **chilly** weather.		
19. Fred's **surly** looks scared people off.		
20. Rita walked rather **anxiously** into the exam room.		

Adverbs

Place an appropriate adverb in each of these sentences – there could be several different answers.

21. _____, Becky answered the first question.

22. Tom _____ wrote his answers down.

23. Clair tidied up the kitchen _____.

24. Peter took out the bags _____.

25. _____, Ramona strode into the room.

26. The nurse _____ attended to her duties.

27. Tom _____ ate his dinner.

28. Despite the bad weather, the boys managed the walk _____.

29. The river ran _____ through the deep gorge.

30. Rick _____ put on his shoes.

31. _____, Natasha ate her ice cream.

32. Lisa performed _____ in the test.

33. Without asking, Jagram _____ ate the sweets.

34. In order to win the race, Gemma ran _____.

35. The wind whistled _____ around the house.

36. The ballerina stepped _____ across the stage.

37. The horses _____ entered the field.

38. Danny missed a chance when he shot _____ at the goalkeeper.

39. Dean _____ made excuses for his naughty behaviour.

40. Bill waited _____ for the trouble to calm down.

/40

Confused words and spellings

> Underline the correct word in each sentence.

1. No one could accept/except the referee's decision.
2. Everyone accept/except the referee knew what was going on.
3. The children were not aloud/allowed to go shopping.
4. The children were heard to complain aloud/allowed when they could not go shopping.
5. "Sack the bored/board!" cried the annoyed fans.
6. "I'm board/bored," said the annoyed fan.
7. The prisoner was out on bale/bail.
8. The cricketer knocked off the bale/bail.
9. "Don't brake/break that vase!" shouted Alice.
10. "Don't use the break/brake like that on the motorway!" cried the instructor.
11. The politicians decided to canvas/canvass opinion.
12. The artist used a canvas/canvass for his portrait.
13. "Check/Cheque your oil," said the mechanic.
14. "Can I pay by check/cheque?" asked the bank customer.
15. Her shoes complemented/complimented her hat, as they were the same colour.
16. Nick complemented/complimented his sister on her choice of hat and dress.
17. The council/counsel were in charge of organising the waste disposal services.
18. The council/counsel gave advice in the courtroom.
19. Tammy had a sweet desert/dessert after her meal.
20. Jonathan had driven all the way across the desert/dessert for his meal.
21. There was a cold draught/draft in the room.
22. Elisha had done the first draft/draught of her essay.
23. The two men fought a dual/duel.
24. The two men had duel/dual responsibility.
25. The ill boy feinted/fainted and had to have medical help.
26. The swordsman feinted/fainted and tricked his opponent into a false move.
27. The Queen formerly/formally announced the opening of Parliament.
28. The Prime Minister had formerly/formally been the Home Secretary.
29. "Hear/Here I am!"
30. "Can you hear/here me?"
31. The lazy boy was described as idle/idol by his boss.
32. The building had a carving of a religious idle/idol outside.

33. The caterpillar produced larva/lava.

34. The volcano produced larva/lava.

35. The shopping bags were as heavy as lead/led.

36. The supporters were led/lead to the ground by a policeman on a motorbike.

37. The skyscraper was struck by lightening/lightning.

38. The pale colours had a lightning/lightening effect on the room.

39. Nobody wanted to lose/loose the cup final.

40. The football manager pulled his tie lose/loose as the game went into extra time.

41. No one knew/new what the result might be.

42. The knew/new members of the team helped us to win.

43. Jenny didn't like filling in personal/personnel information on the form.

44. The personal/personnel department dealt with recruitment.

45. Fiona didn't like travelling on a plane/plain.

46. The open country was very plane/plain.

47. The hunters chased their pray/prey.

48. The vicar asked the congregation to pray/prey.

49. "Keep quiet/quite!" whispered the guide.

50. "That's quite/quiet enough, thank you," muttered the teacher.

51. The king's reign/rain only lasted a few months.

52. The rain/reign spoiled the king's visit.

53. "Which is the rite/right/write answer?" asked the professor.

54. "Rite/Right/Write down the correct answer," he continued.

55. "Get out of my site/sight!" yelled the annoyed man.

56. "Is this the correct site/sight for the archaeological dig?" asked Anil.

57. "That car is definitely stationery/stationary," said the policeman.

58. "Can I buy stationery/stationary from here?" asked the office worker.

59. The weather/whether was terrible in the Rocky Mountains.

60. No one knew weather/whether to go on the walk or not.

/50

Double letter words

Can you write in the missing word in each case?
All of these words have a double **b** in them.

1.   An a _____ is a shortened down form of a word.

2.   If you b_____, it means you talk a lot of nonsense.

3.   If you d_____, you have a go, or an attempt, at something, often to try it out.

4.   If you g_____, you eat your food quickly.

5.   If you h_____, you've probably hurt your leg.

6.   If you have a h_____, it's usually something you do in your spare time.

7.   A p_____ is a hard stone, often smooth to the touch.

8.   A r_____ is a small, furry creature with big, floppy ears.

9.   If you s_____, you don't write very tidily.

10. If you are s_____, it means you won't change your mind easily.

This time the words have a double **c** in them.

11. To increase speed is to a_____.

12. An extra item that often complements a main object is an a_____.

13. When something goes wrong unintentionally, it is an a_____.

14. A place in which to live or inhabit is called a_____.

15. When you have achieved something you say that it has been a_____.

16. When something is precise, it is said to be a_____.

17. If someone or something is a bit unusual and quirky, it is described as e_____.

18. When something happens, but not very often, we say it happens o_____.

19. A person's job is called their o_____.

20. A substance found in cigarettes and smoked in pipes is called t _____.

These words have either double **d**, double **f** or double **g**.

21. The name, or number, of the place where someone lives is their a_____.

22. A common name for a violin – it also means to twist the rules – is a f_____.

23. Some people who travel too high up get g_____.

24. Water formed in a small hollow in the ground is a p_____.

25. A feeling similar to love is a_____.

26. A drink that usually contains caffeine and can be instant or made from beans is c_____.

27. When something is enough, it is s_____.

28. A person who asks for money is a b_____.

29. Items that you take with you on holiday or on a journey are called l_____.

30. A kind of sled is a t_____.

A mixture of different double consonants!

31. A place under a building, often used for storage – c_____.

32. Straight away – i_____.

33. The start of something – b_____.

34. A sport involving rackets, sometimes played on grass – t_____.

35. The desire for something, usually associated with food – a_____.

36. The person you compete against – o_____.

37. An extremely strong wind, usually found in the tropics – h_____.

38. A place from where raw materials are dug from the ground – q_____.

39. A name given for an extended piece of writing on a particular topic – e_____.

40. A document needed to gain entry to a country that you are not a native of – p_____.

/40

Silent letter words

In each of the sentences below, there is a word with a silent letter missing. Underline the word and rewrite it with its missing letter.

1. The builder hit his thum with the hammer. _____

2. No one douted that the answer was correct. _____

3. The forward feined injury to get a penalty. _____

4. The girl's legs were covered with nat bites. _____

5. Nobody new what was up with the new boy. _____

6. Thomas did not get a receit for the presents he bought. _____

7. Robert had a seudonym on the internet message board, to hide his identity. _____

8. It was cold so Catherine rapped up warm. _____

9. The angry dog nashed its teeth. _____

10. The famous film star rote in Jemma's autograph book. _____

In the passage below are ten words with a silent **b** in them. Underline the 10 words.

11–20. Barry broke the table when an earthquake that felt like a bomb went off. He climbed back into his chair and combed his hair, which had been messed up in the explosion. A few crumbs from his dinner floated in the air and landed, without doubt, on his knee. His face and both his upper limbs were numb with shock, but he kept calm. He wondered whether the plumbing in the house had been affected. He was certainly indebted to the strong table for protecting him from the quake, although his thumb had been trapped and squashed by it.

Here are 10 words that contain a silent **k** and their meanings. Match the words with their meanings.

21. knight   a tied coil of thread or perhaps rope

22. knave   bang on something

23. knit   be aware of

24. knee   an item used to cut things

25. knot   a word implying that someone is of low class or a troublemaker

26. know   the mid-way joint on the leg

27. knock   a finger joint

28. knowledge   someone who might have worn armour, who has the title "Sir"

29. knife   awareness

30. knuckle   to create material from thread, often with needles

Write **correct** or **incorrect** to say which of the following words are spelled correctly.

31. matress – something you lie on   _____

32. attitude – an opinion or feeling towards something   _____

33. narled – twisted and old looking   _____

34. foreigner – a person not from where you live   _____

35. neumonia – a disease   _____

36. sychiatrist – a person who tries to understand the workings of a person's mind   _____

37. wrinkle – a bendy line, often in skin   _____

38. pseudonym – a made up name   _____

39. plumer – a person who fixes baths, taps and pipes   _____

40. psychic – a person who can see into the future and/or read minds   _____

/40

Gh/ph/ch words

Look at these words which have **gh** in them. Tick whether they are silent, pronounced as **f** or pronounced as **g**. The first example is done for you.

Word	Silent	Pronounced f	Pronounced g
borough	✔		
1. cough			
2. ghoul			
3. dough			
4. sight			
5. enough			
6. ghetto			
7. tough			
8. nought			
9. trough			
10. fought			

Unscramble the following words which have a **ph** sound in them. The first example is done for you.

Word	Meaning	Answer
hspae	a period of time	phase
11. than mop	a ghost	
12. chain yips	a doctor	
13. ash rep	part of a sentence	
14. pics shy	a scientific subject	
15. pasta hen	a game bird	
16. para tough	a signature	
17. heap pit	a short text honouring a dead person	
18. rag hap par	a block of text on one topic, subject or idea	
19. cheap ton	a tomb or monument for a person or people whose remains are elsewhere	
20. hum trip	a significant achievement	

Answer booklet English 10 Minute tests

Test 1
1. boy
2. girl, make-up
3. bands
4. river, banks, town
5. feet
6. rain, umbrella
7. puppy, chair
8. canoes, rivers
9. desk
10. answers, class
11. cars, trains, girls
12. hat
13. soldiers, monument
14. goldfish
15. boy, sandwiches
16. day
17. happiness
18. intelligence
19. boredom
20. bravery
21. kindness
22. love
23. courage
24. joy
25. imagination, fear
26. Beauty
27. Revenge
28. loneliness
29. loyalty
30. skill
31–40. Concrete common nouns: riverbank, log, water, clouds and sky. Abstract common nouns: fear, nervousness, threat, anger and sadness
41. boys
42. trip
43. imagination
44. players
45. session
46. entry
47. amazement
48. worry
49. dream
50. coach

Test 2
1. Colorado
2. United States
3. Estes Park
4. Rocky Mountain National Park
5. Lyons
6. Denver
7. Louisiana
8. Hurricane Gustav
9. England
10. Nick
11–20. Common nouns: college, guitar, motorway. Proper nouns: Arthur, Edinburgh, George, Andy. Words that are not nouns: stupid, random, several
21–45. Many answers are possible.

Test 3
1. girls
2. churches
3. ages
4. exams
5. bullies
6. wives
7. lenses
8. taxes
9. losses
10. fairies
11. elves
12. sandwiches
13. loaves
14. teeth
15. armies
16. sheep
17. men
18. thieves
19. selves
20. batches
21. girls
22. ponies
23. chimneys
24. witnesses
25. people
26. themselves
27. houses
28. strawberries
29. stories
30. mosquitoes
31. analyses
32. stimuli
33. axes
34. crises
35. oxen
36. oases
37. women
38. media (irregular), mediums (regular)
39. deer
40. lice
41. children
42. cacti (irregular), cactuses (regular)
43. fish (irregular), fishes (regular)
44. species
45. geese
46. moose
47. offspring
48. emphases
49. scissors
50. mice
51–60. Many answers are possible, but the story must include the following words: dogs, cats, owners, houses, streets, trees, habits, pets, complaints, gardens.

Test 4
1. He
2. her
3. We
4. it
5. She
6. It
7. She
8. them
9. them
10. They
11. him
12. it
13. She
14. him
15. They
16. she
17. her
18. She
19. it
20. him
21. them
22. her
23. them
24. him
25. it
26. her
27. it
28. them
29. her
30. us

Test 5
1. ran
2. realise
3. Eating
4. shake
5. spoiled
6. speak
7. eat
8. smiled
9. exploded
10. shouted
11–20. Many answers are possible, but each sentence must include an appropriate verb.
21–40. Just a verb: decommission
Just a noun: silliness, sympathy, table, questioning, document
Both: run, joke, cry, fear, show, talk, smell, study, dump
Neither: happy, pretty, clever, blissful, awkwardly

Test 6
1. was running
2. were organising
3. is coming
4. are going
5. are
6. are working
7. was
8. are
9. were
10. is getting
11–20. Correct agreement: 12, 14, 15, 18, 20
Incorrect agreement: 11, 13, 16, 17, 19
21. is
22. were
23. was
24. was
25. is
26. is
27. was
28. is
29. was
30. is
31–40. Many answers are possible, but sentences must include the words from questions 21–30.

Test 7
1. ate
2. performed
3. stood
4. rode
5. had
6. giggled
7. sang
8. invented
9. sat
10. knitted
11. I have found / I found
12. I have studied / I studied
13. I have taught / I taught
14. I have done / I did
15. I have called / I called
16. I have shouted / I shouted
17. I have caught / I caught
18. I have clapped / I clapped
19. I have brought / I brought
20. I have gone / I went
21. The football team were losing at half time.
22. Chuck sang and played guitar in a band.
23. Catherine bought strange clothes.
24. Liam wore fancy dress costumes at parties.
25. Laura rarely asked questions.
26. Isaac smiled a lot, especially when he concentrated.
27. Whitney's loud voice filled the room.
28. Ari walked into the classroom when she was ready.
29. Samuel invested in internet based companies.
30. Maisie enjoyed school holidays because she could lie in.

Test 8
1. dull, dreary
2. happy
3. exciting
4. cute
5. tall, imposing
6. expensive
7. loud
8. skilful
9. fashionable
10. humorous
11–20. Many answers are possible.
21–30. Many answers are possible, but the adjectives used should help to build up a mysterious and spooky mood.
31–40. Many answers are possible, but the adjectives used should help to build up a light-hearted and jolly mood.
41–50. Many answers are possible, but the adjectives used should help to build up an action-packed mood.

Test 9

A	C	K	E	N	C	O	U	R	A	G	E	F	X	E	P	K	P	Q	C
P	H	R	Q	G	T	G	C	H	K	F	X	I	E	G	N	X	T	B	V
V	L	U	M	S	U	D	I	O	D	N	H	N	Q	M	E	T	L	T	L
N	J	K	R	X	L	T	V	W	C	K	J	I	U	W	W	X	T	M	V
U	T	O	R	P	W	S	N	Q	H	R	J	S	A	V	U	X	R	E	B
M	F	J	O	A	A	R	W	K	W	N	E	H	F	G	O	K	S	O	I
B	Z	G	B	W	C	B	B	A	F	H	S	A	I	R	Y	K	O	E	C
I	D	Y	P	P	H	E	T	K	N	A	I	N	T	U	N	V	X	H	I
U	E	B	U	M	Z	M	W	Y	I	Z	M	S	W	E	I	I	P	R	S
R	U	N	V	J	I	J	I	F	C	T	I	T	K	L	A	T	S	B
K	F	B	W	M	W	P	N	V	D	N	K	G	H	L	N	L	O	R	W
U	V	U	V	D	G	M	X	N	L	G	A	H	F	B	E	R	L	P	V
S	F	I	N	D	W	D	E	E	D	D	T	L	L	G	C	O	W	U	G
R	L	C	Q	R	R	Y	A	P	Y	L	K	T	W	X	R	Y	F	K
E	A	H	W	U	O	R	A	O	A	T	A	E	B	A	C	X	A	S	J
D	F	E	H	C	E	I	J	Y	R	S	P	P	K	T	Q	X	J	F	J
N	L	E	S	P	U	W	B	X	T	D	B	A	Y	O	P	W	G	J	Y
A	Y	R	O	F	J	O	F	G	U	Y	G	N	L	R	I	E	T	N	P
W	T	A	C	K	L	E	K	D	E	S	O	L	E	F	I	H	S	F	G
P	T	I	N	J	U	R	E	G	X	W	S	P	M	L	B	J	A	K	Q

1

Test 10

The crossword contains: NERVOUS, MASSIVE, ANGRY, MOOD, GLOOM, BRIGHT, QUIET, INCREDIBLE, MIRROR, HORROR, HAPPY, PLEASANT, IMPOSSIBLE, RELUCTANT, CLEVER, INJURED, COOPED, SPECIAL, COLD, BEAUTIFUL, SCARED

Test 11
1.	quickly	2.	amazingly
3.	reluctantly	4.	lazily
5.	Astonishingly	6.	Luckily
7.	fortunately	8.	cleverly
9.	crazily	10.	cautiously

11–20. Sentences with ly adverb: 12, 15, 16, 20
Sentences with ly adjective: 11, 13, 14, 17, 18, 19

21–40. Many answers are possible.

Test 12
1.	accept	2.	except
3.	allowed	4.	aloud
5.	board	6.	bored
7.	bail	8.	bale
9.	break	10.	brake
11.	canvass	12.	canvas
13.	check	14.	cheque
15.	complemented	16.	complimented
17.	council	18.	counsel
19.	dessert	20.	desert
21.	draught	22.	draft
23.	duel	24.	dual
25.	fainted	26.	feinted
27.	formally	28.	formerly
29.	Here	30.	hear
31.	idle	32.	idol
33.	larva	34.	lava
35.	lead	36.	led
37.	lightning	38.	lightening
39.	lose	40.	loose
41.	knew	42.	new
43.	personal	44.	personnel
45.	plane	46.	plain
47.	prey	48.	pray
49.	quiet	50.	quite
51.	reign	52.	rain
53.	right	54.	Write
55.	sight	56.	site
57.	stationary	58.	stationery
59.	weather	60.	whether

Test 13
1.	abbreviation	2.	babble
3.	dabble	4.	gobble
5.	hobble	6.	hobby
7.	pebble	8.	rabbit
9.	scribble	10.	stubborn

11. accelerate
12. accompaniment or accessory
13. accident
14. accommodation
| 15. | accomplished | 16. | accurate |

Test 14
1.	thumb	2.	doubted
3.	feigned	4.	gnat
5.	knew	6.	receipt
7.	pseudonym	8.	wrapped
9.	gnashed	10.	wrote
11.	bomb	12.	climbed
13.	combed	14.	crumbs
15.	doubt	16.	limbs
17.	numb	18.	plumbing
19.	indebted	20.	thumb

21. knight – someone who might have worn armour, who has the title "Sir"
22. knave – a word implying that someone is of low class or a troublemaker
23. knit – to create material from thread, often with needles
24. knee – the mid-way joint on the leg
25. knot – a tied coil of thread or perhaps rope
26. know – be aware of
27. knock – bang on something
28. knowledge – awareness
29. knife – an item used to cut things
30. knuckle – a finger joint
31–40. Words spelt correctly: 32, 34, 37, 38, 40
Words spelt incorrectly: 31, 33, 35, 36, 39

Test 15
1–10. Words with a silent **gh**: dough, sight, nought, fought
Words with **gh** pronounced f: cough, enough, tough, trough
Words with **gh** pronounced g: ghoul, ghetto
11.	phantom	12.	physician
13.	phrase	14.	physics
15.	pheasant	16.	autograph
17.	epitaph	18.	paragraph
19.	cenotaph	20.	triumph

21–30. Words with a soft **ch** sound: machinery, treachery, which, sandwich, quench
Words with a hard **ch** sound: anarchy, chemist, chord, school, echoes

31–40. Many answers are possible, but the five sentences should include the words used in questions 21–30.

Test 16
1. under water – submarine
2. a lower or lesser culture – subculture
3. a total below the main one – subtotal
4. below zero – subzero
5. something fallen to a lower level – subsidence
6. headings lower than the main ones – subheadings
7. a meaning below the main one – subtext
8. under cover – subterfuge
9. lower levels – sublevels
10. below the main soil – subsoil
11. unnecessary
12. immature
13. irregular
14. unhappy
15. immoral
16. unclean
17. disinterested or uninterested
18. unclear
19. disconnect
20. unload
21. disobey
22. imprecise
23. non-fiction
24. disproportionate
25. unlucky
26. impossible
27. unfortunate
28. unintelligent
29. unfazed
30. inconspicuous
31–40. Many answers are possible, but they could include:
31. reconsider, reproduce
32. international, intertwine
33. postpone, post-mortem
34. declassify, debunk
35. anti-climax, antidote
36. mistake, misfortune
37. hyperactive, hypertension
38. television, telephone
39. automotive, automobile
40. disrupt, disobey
41. retake
42. inappropriate
43. disappeared
44. extraterrestrial
45. substitute

Test 17
1. agreement
2. action
3. painter, painting
4. servant, service
5. formula, formation
6. building, builder
7. informer, information
8. creation, creator
9. encouragement
10. conference
11. reinvention
12. living, livestock
13. fastening, fastener
14. application
15. reversing, reversal
16. reader, readathon
17. plumber, plumbing
18. implication
19. interaction, interacting
20. dismissal
21–30. Suffix used correctly: 22, 25, 29
Suffix used incorrectly: 21, 23, 24, 26, 27, 28, 30
31. waxy
32. sandy
33. childish, childlike
34. clueless
35. amazing
36. reasonable
37. harmless, harmful
38. beautiful, beauteous
39. famous
40. continued, continual, continuous
41. shiny, shining
42. spotty, spotted
43. scandalous
44. calmness
45. bookish
46. economical

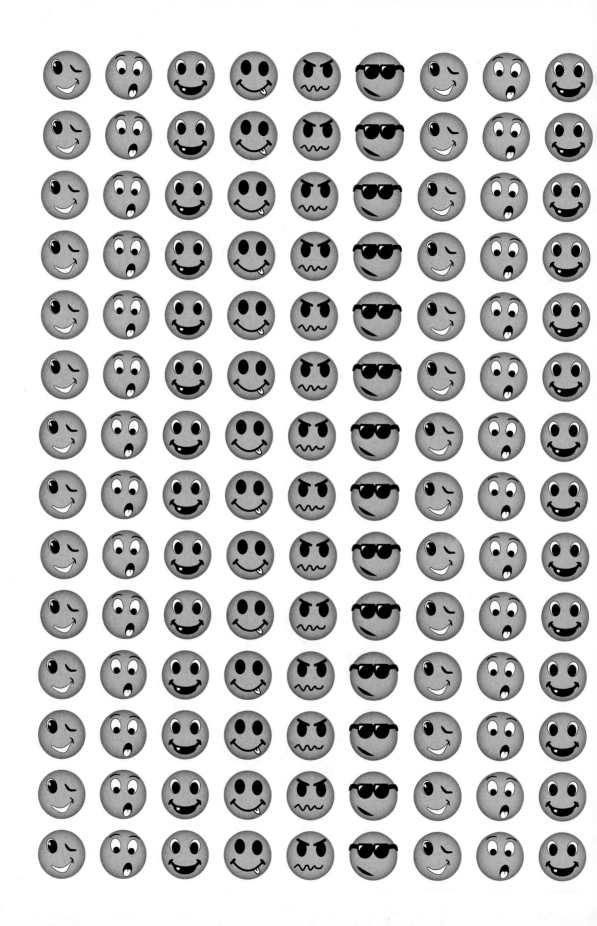

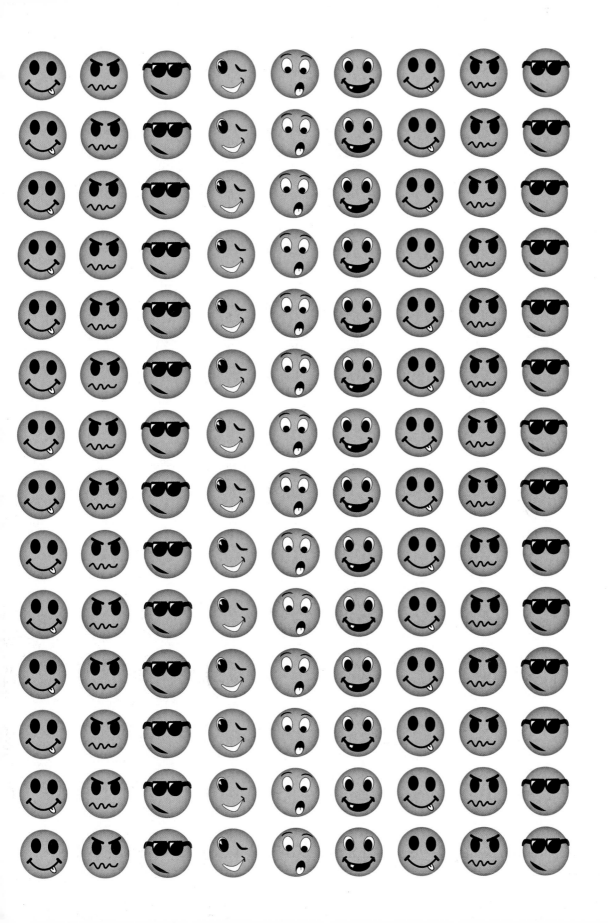

47. reputable
48. useful, useless
49. considerate, considerable
50. revolutionary

Test 18

1–10. Everyone who dreams of being a superstar musician wants the money and the fame, but how many people want all the day to day hassles that go with such status? **I**magine never being able to go to your local supermarket in your scruffy clothes and saying hello to **J**ackie who works on the tills. **I**magine never being able to visit your relatives without making an appointment, because the paparazzi will be expecting you to turn up at your **U**ncle **A**lbert's house. **W**ouldn't that be awful? **Y**ou might say that having six-figure pay cheques might cancel all that out, but **I** wouldn't like it. **OK**, so you're number one in the charts and the **BBC** want you to do an interview – that's fine, but you can't even walk down the street to the local store to buy a new comb to make sure that you look the part!

11. The Rocky Mountain National Park is in Colorado.
12. Louisiana is a state in the south of the USA.
13. Manchester has two football teams, City and United.
14. Mr Bloggs eats biscuits made in Scotland.
15. Jeremy went to Spain for his Easter holiday.
16. Christmas is celebrated in December.
17. Greenland is a very large country.
18. The school held its special assembly in the hall.
19. Lucie and Ellie ate cabbage reluctantly.
20. CD players will be obsolete in the future.
21–40. Many answers are possible.

Test 19

1. The captain spoke to the crew. He told them that all was well.
2. Vicky got in touch with a long-lost friend. She hadn't seen him for years.
3. Puppies are cute. They do make a mess though.
4. Europe is a continent. Africa is also a continent.
5. The band came from Melbourne in Australia. Melbourne in Australia is well-known for producing good bands.
6. Dave ran. He didn't want to miss the bus.
7. Michelle visited her friend. She didn't want to, really.
8. Emma went to the seaside. Her hair was messed up by the wind.
9. The new girl settled into the school. She knew some of the people there.
10. The library had thousands of books. They didn't have the one that Nick wanted, however.
11. The volcano erupted. Lava shot out into the sky.
12. The sea was calm. The ships didn't move.
13. Faye put on her make-up. It didn't make her feel better.
14. Jon sang beautifully. His friends sang too.
15. Sally and Nora made dinner. They cooked turnips and cabbage.
16. Rodney played his favourite music. No one liked it.
17. Jasmine bought lots of new clothes. She

wore them.
18. The team lost. They played badly.
19. The oil painting was valuable. It had been damaged.
20. The girls went riding. It was raining.
21. Singing wasn't Mike's favourite activity. He got embarrassed.
22. Shopping online is easy. You have to wait for the goods to arrive.
23. The toys didn't work. They were brand new.
24. Alicia did her homework. She did it badly.
25. David was in a band. They were very good.
26–30. Many answers are possible, but sentences should include the words given in the question.

Test 20

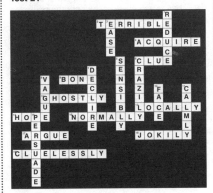

Test 21

Test 22

1. Emma bought beans, cabbages and potatoes for dinner.
2. Despite being very clever, Agnes got low marks on the test.
3. Sally, Joe and the others emptied the car for their mum.
4. All people have talents, but some have more useful talents than others.
5. Priya was a great runner, despite getting blisters easily.
6. Unfortunately, Joe didn't revise properly.
7. Nadia bought shoes, shoes and more shoes in the sale.
8. Fred, despite his youth, did extremely well in the competition.
9. Betty, although she came last, enjoyed the marathon run.

10. Whenever she pressed the bell, she got a slight electric shock.
11–20. Sentences with correctly used commas: 11, 13, 14, 17, 18, 19
Sentences with incorrectly used commas: 12, 15, 16, 20
21. "Why can't I tie this knot properly?" muttered Jim.
22. "Look out!" warned Anastasia.
23. " Which of these should I wear?" asked Danielle.
24. "Land ahoy! Over there!" screamed the ship's watch.
25. "Matthew – why are you asking Amy?" said the teacher.
26. "Ow! That hurt!" complained Jade.
27. "Is that you, Aaron?" asked Adam.
28. "Don't touch that, James!" yelled the PE teacher.
29. "Rebecca! Goodness gracious!" said her startled sister.
30. "Where is your homework?" said the teacher to David.
31. "Brittany! No!" raged the team manager.
32. "How did you manage to work that out?" asked Steven.
33. "Did your photographs come out OK?" remarked Kamal.
34. "Watch my fingers!" warned Louis.
35. "You're fired!" shouted Bill.
36. "Why am I fired?" asked Dean.
37. "Because of all the mistakes you made!" retorted Bill, angrily.
38. "Why didn't you sack the others who made mistakes?" replied Dean.
39. "Listen to me!" screeched Bill.
40. "Why should I listen to someone who shouts all the time?" muttered Dean as he left.

Test 23

1. didn't
2. wasn't
3. wasn't
4. couldn't
5. wouldn't
6. isn't
7. hadn't
8. could've
9. should've, he'd
10. hadn't
11. We'll
12. Can't
13. didn't
14. I'm
15. You'll
16. should've, he'd, didn't
17. didn't, wouldn't
18. didn't
19. I'll
20. hadn't, couldn't
21. didn't
22. wouldn't
23. Laura's
24. couldn't
25. You're
26–35. Sentences with correctly used apostrophes: 26, 29, 30, 33, 35
Sentences with incorrectly used apostrophes: 27, 28, 31, 32, 34
36. should've
37. won't
38. isn't
39. we'll
40. I've
41. you'll
42. they've
43. hadn't
44. he'd
45. she'd

3

Test 24

1. "Pass the ball over here," yelled Domenico.
2. "Out!" declared the umpire.
3. "Where are my toys?" mused Ben.
4. "I think I know the answer," remarked Sam.
5. "That book was amazing," declared Lizzie.
6. "Tony! Come here and see this!" shouted Phil, excitedly.
7. "Wait," said Harry, "I think I can hear something."
8. "What is it? I hope it's not scary," mumbled Hannah.
9. "Maisie – tuck your shirt in!" yelled the teacher.
10. "Why don't you borrow Abigail's book?" suggested Richard.
11–20. Sentences with correct punctuation: 11, 13, 14, 16, 17, 20
Sentences with incorrect punctuation: 12, 15, 18, 19
21–30. Many answers are possible, but speech marks and other punctuation should be used correctly.

Test 25

1. their
2. There
3. there
4. Their
5. They're
6. their
7. There
8. Their
9. They're
10. They're, their
11–20. Sentences with **there/their/they're** used correctly: 13, 16, 18, 19, 20
Sentences with **there/their/they're** used incorrectly: 11, 12, 14, 15, 17
21–26. Many answers are possible, but they must be used correctly in each sentence.
27–33. Many answers are possible, but **their** must be used correctly in each sentence.
34–40. Many answers are possible, but **there** must be used correctly in each sentence.

Test 26

1. excepted
2. adapted
3. allusion
4. Always
5. bare
6. border
7. coarse
8. industrial
9. Leant
10. morale
11. accepted
12. adopted
13. illusion
14. All ways
15. bear
16. boarder
17. course
18. industrious
19. Lent
20. moral
21. alcohol
22. appearance
23. eighth
24. beautiful
25. business
26. cemetery
27. committee
28. deteriorate
29. handkerchief
30. laboratory
31. loneliness
32. marriage
33. necessary
34. neighbour
35. pursue
36. scissors
37. sentence
38. soldier
39. weird
40. villain

Test 27

1–10. first paragraph (lines 1–3) – This paragraph explains why having few instruments is important.
second paragraph (lines 3–7) – This paragraph explains why having easy songs is important.
third paragraph (lines 7–10) – This paragraph talks about stories in folk music.
fourth paragraph (lines 11–13) – This paragraph talks about why unfashionable folk music is good.
fifth paragraph (lines 14–17) – This paragraph talks about how folk music connects us to the past.
sixth paragraph (lines 17–20) – This paragraph talks about how folk music doesn't need expensive equipment.
seventh paragraph (lines 21–24) – This paragraph gives personal reasons for liking folk music.
eighth paragraph (lines 24–28) – This paragraph talks about the cost of attending folk concerts.
ninth paragraph (lines 28–33) – This paragraph talks about how folk music brings you close to the performers.
tenth paragraph (lines 33–35) – This paragraph sums up the writer's feelings about folk music.

Test 28

1. replied
2. cried
3. fortified
4. spied
5. tried
6. edified
7. clarified
8. replied
9. dried
10. fried
11. laid
12. paid
13. enjoyed
14. portrayed
15. said
16. bought
17. prayed
18. volleyed
19. relied
20. carried
21. butterflies
22. donkeys
23. journeys
24. cries
25. tries
26. ladies
27. days
28. puppies
29. guys
30. cities
31. toys
32. ponies
33. valleys
34. companies
35. plays
36. turkeys
37. pantries
38. bakeries
39. qualities
40. skies
41. stupefy
42. rectify
43. baby
44. beauty
45. fry
46. heavy
47. early
48. tray
49. mollify
50. spy
51–60. Many answers are possible, but each sentence must include a noun ending in **y**.

Test 29

1. bones
2. hopes
3. advances
4. notices
5. absences
6. bandages
7. battles
8. carbohydrates
9. stockpiles
10. pickles
11. advancement
12. persuasion
13. declaration
14. reduction
15. supposition
16. acquisition
17. freedom
18. exploration
19. exercise
20. disposition
21. divorce
22. drape
23. downsize
24. sleaze
25. compare
26. fertilise
27. impure
28. cease
29. capable
30. joke
31. true
32. whole
33. clue
34. courage
35. notice
36. peace
37. mate
38. dissuade
39. due
40. like
41–50. Many answers are possible, but each sentence must include a noun ending in **e**.

Test 30

1. a
2. b
3. c
4. d
5. a
6. b
7. c
8. b
9. d
10. d

The following words contain a **ch** sound, but is it a hard sound, as in **monarch**, or a soft sound, as in **church** or **moustache**? An example has been done for you.

Word	Soft	Hard
avalanche	✔	
21. anarchy		
22. machinery		
23. treachery		
24. chemist		
25. which		
26. chord		
27. sandwich		
28. school		
29. echoes		
30. quench		

31–40. Write five sentences, with each sentence using two of the words in questions 21–30.

_____

_____

_____

_____

_____

/40

Prefixes

Match up the definitions with the correct words, using lines to join up the pairs.

1. under water   subheadings

2. a lower or lesser culture   subtext

3. a total below the main one   sublevels

4. below zero   submarine

5. something fallen to a lower level   subsoil

6. headings lower than the main ones   subtotal

7. a meaning below the main one   subculture

8. under cover   subzero

9. lower levels   subsidence

10. below the main soil   subterfuge

Add a prefix to all of these words to form a word with an opposite meaning.

11. necessary _____   12. mature _____

13. regular _____   14. happy _____

15. moral _____   16. clean _____

17. interested _____   18. clear _____

19. connect _____   20. load _____

21. obey _____   22. precise _____

23. fiction _____   24. proportionate _____

25. lucky _____   26. possible _____

27. fortunate _____   28. intelligent _____

29. fazed _____   30. conspicuous _____

Make two words for each of these prefixes. There are lots of possible answers.

31. re _____ _____

32. inter _____ _____

33. post _____ _____

34. de _____ _____

35. anti _____ _____

36. mis _____ _____

37. hyper _____ _____

38. tele _____ _____

39. auto _____ _____

40. dis _____ _____

Complete these sentences by inserting the correct word with a prefix from the list below.

inappropriate   disappeared   extraterrestrial   retake   substitute

41. John had to _____ the test.

42. The pupils were expelled for _____ behaviour.

43. The car _____ around the corner.

44. Flying saucers are an example of _____ life.

45. Because of an injury, a _____ had to take over.

/45

Change these verbs into nouns by adding a suffix.
Some may have more than one possible change.

Example – do (verb)   do + er = doer (noun)

1.   agree   _____

2.   act   _____

3.   paint   _____

4.   serve   _____

5.   form   _____

6.   build   _____

7.   inform   _____

8.   create   _____

9.   encourage   _____

10.   confer   _____

11.   reinvent   _____

12.   live   _____

13.   fasten   _____

14.   apply   _____

15.   reverse   _____

16.   read   _____

17.   plumb   _____

18.   imply   _____

19.   interact   _____

20.   dismiss   _____

In these sentences, the underlined words have a suffix. Write **correct** or
incorrect by each word to say whether the suffix has been used correctly.

21.   The boys read the <u>informer</u> on the wall.   _____

22.   The <u>information</u> on the topic was inadequate.   _____

23.   The <u>dismissation</u> of the player was expected because of his bad foul.   _____

24.   The <u>removation</u> of the offending spider from the room cheered
       up the nervous children.   _____

25.   The <u>inspiration</u> for the story was quite unexpected.   _____

26. The boy's <u>refusage</u> to do his homework shocked the teacher. _____

27. The <u>inspiral</u> for the painting was a similar piece by a famous artist. _____

28. The <u>assemblage</u> of the different parts was more difficult than
    expected. _____

29. The <u>renovation</u> of the house was incredibly successful. _____

30. The <u>facinatedness</u> of the children increased as they toured
    through the zoo. _____

> Add suffixes to these words to turn them into adjectives.
> Some may have more than one possible answer.

31.	wax	_____	32.	sand	_____

31. wax   _____   32. sand   _____

33. child   _____   34. clue   _____

35. amaze   _____   36. reason   _____

37. harm   _____   38. beauty   _____

39. fame   _____   40. continue   _____

41. shine   _____   42. spot   _____

43. scandal   _____   44. calm   _____

45. book   _____   46. economy   _____

47. repute   _____   48. use   _____

49. consider   _____   50. revolution _____

/50

Capital letters

Read this passage. There are 10 lots of capital letters missing.
Underline the words which should have capital letters.

1–10.   everyone who dreams of being a superstar musician wants the money and the fame, but
        how many people want all the day to day hassles that go with such status? imagine never
        being able to go to your local supermarket in your scruffy clothes and saying hello to
        jackie who works on the tills. imagine never being able to visit your relatives without
        making an appointment, because the paparazzi will be expecting you to turn up at your
        uncle albert's house. wouldn't that be awful? you might say that having six-figure pay
        cheques would cancel all that out, but i wouldn't like it. ok, so you're number one in the
        charts and the bbc want you to do an interview – that's fine, but you can't even walk down
        the street to buy a new comb to make sure that you look the part!

In these sentences, all of the words have capital letters. Re-write them
so that there is the correct number of words with capitals in each one.

11.   The Rocky Mountain National Park Is In Colorado.

      _____

12.   Louisiana Is A State In The South Of The USA.

      _____

13.   Manchester Has Two Football Teams, City And United.

      _____

14.   Mr Bloggs Eats Biscuits Made In Scotland.

      _____

15.   Jeremy Went To Spain For His Easter Holiday.

      _____

16.   Christmas Is Celebrated In December.

      _____

17.   Greenland Is A Very Large Country.

      _____

18. The School Held Its Special Assembly In The Hall.

_____

19. Lucie And Ellie Ate Cabbage Reluctantly.

_____

20. CD Players Will Be Obsolete In The Future.

_____

> Write down two words that need capital letters for each of the categories below. There are lots of different answers you could use.

21. A boy's name   _____   _____
22. A girl's name   _____   _____
23. A street name   _____   _____
24. A name of a country in Europe   _____   _____
25. A name of a city in America   _____   _____
26. A name that might be given to a pet dog or cat _____   _____
27. A name of a planet   _____   _____
28. A name of a television programme   _____   _____
29. A name of a famous film star   _____   _____
30. A name of a famous musician or band   _____   _____
31. A name of a supermarket or shop   _____   _____
32. A name of a company or organisation   _____   _____
33. A name of a famous mountain   _____   _____
34. A name of a famous historical figure   _____   _____
35. A name of a famous battle from history   _____   _____
36. A name of a magazine   _____   _____
37. A name of a river   _____   _____
38. A name of a country in Africa   _____   _____
39. A name of a famous author   _____   _____
40. A name of a school   _____   _____

/40

In these examples, there are two sentences that need to be separated by a full stop. Put in the full stop where you think it should go.

1. The captain spoke to the crew he told them that all was well.
2. Vicky got in touch with a long-lost friend she hadn't seen him for years.
3. Puppies are cute they do make a mess though.
4. Europe is a continent Africa is also a continent.
5. The band came from Melbourne in Australia Melbourne in Australia is well-known for producing good bands.
6. Dave ran he didn't want to miss the bus.
7. Michelle visited her friend she didn't want to, really.
8. Emma went to the seaside her hair was messed up by the wind.
9. The new girl settled into the school she knew some of the people there.
10. The library had thousands of books they didn't have the one that Nick wanted, however.
11. The volcano erupted lava shot out into the sky.
12. The sea was calm the ships didn't move.
13. Faye put on her make-up it didn't make her feel better.
14. Jon sang beautifully his friends sang too.
15. Sally and Nora made dinner they cooked turnips and cabbage.

Here are some sentences which have been joined by a connective. Take out the connective and make them into two separate sentences, using a full stop.

16. Rodney played music, but no one liked it.

_____

17. Jasmine bought lots of new clothes and wore them.

_____

18. The team lost because they played badly.

_____

19. The oil painting was valuable but it had been damaged.

_____

20. The girls went riding although it was raining.

_____

21. Singing wasn't Mike's favourite activity, because he got embarrassed.

_____

22. Shopping online is easy, but you have to wait for the goods to arrive.

_____

23. The toys didn't work although they were brand new.

_____

24. Alicia did her homework, but she did it badly.

_____

25. David was in a band and they were very good.

_____

Write a short story of your own, in five sentences. In each sentence you should use the word that you have been given for that sentence. Build up the sentences into one complete story that makes sense. The first sentence has been done for you, so do five after that. Make sure you put a full stop at the end of each sentence.

danger Rodney didn't want to go on the expedition, because he knew he would be in danger.

26. after

_____

27. car

_____

28. skid

_____

29. knee

_____

30. sit

_____

/30

Prefixes and suffixes

Find the words at the bottom of the page in the word search. They may be found backwards, forwards, up, down or diagonally in any direction.

INTERACT	PREVIEW	STATION
REVISE	ADMISSION	DESCRIBE
DISMISS	TORRENT	INSTANT
EXPENSE	HORRIBLE	APPROVAL
CONJOIN	BETWEEN	FLORIST
MICROSCOPE	MULTIPLE	NORMAL
SEPARATE	REBATE	

Fill in the crossword with words ending in **ly** or **e** using the clues to help you.

Across

2. Really bad
4. Get hold of
6. Hint
9. Part of a skeleton
12. Like a ghost
13. Nearby
14. Wish for
16. Usually
17. Disagree
18. In a non-serious manner
19. Without any idea

Down

1. Make smaller
3. Comfort or simplicity
5. In a way that uses common sense
6. In an unpredictable manner
7. Announce, often in public
8. Unclear, imprecise
10. The front of your head
11. In a relaxed manner
15. Get someone to change their mind

Commas, question marks and exclamation marks

Put in the commas in these sentences.

1. Emma bought beans cabbages and potatoes for dinner.

2. Despite being very clever Agnes got low marks on the test.

3. Sally Joe and the others emptied the car for their mum.

4. All people have talents but some have more useful talents than others.

5. Priya was a great runner despite getting blisters easily.

6. Unfortunately Joe didn't revise properly.

7. Nadia bought shoes shoes and more shoes in the sale.

8. Fred despite his youth did extremely well in the competition.

9. Betty although she came last enjoyed the marathon run.

10. Whenever she pressed the bell she got a slight electric shock.

Look at the sentences in this table and tick to show whether or not the commas are in the correct places. The first one is done for you as an example.

sentence	correctly used commas	incorrectly used commas
Eventually, James got the answer.	✔	
11. Mia ate the biscuits, but left the bread.		
12. Laura, ate the bread but left the biscuits.		
13. Hannah, despite being inexperienced, won the match for the girls.		
14. Cara didn't like her present, despite it being expensive.		
15. Josh, played the bass.		
16. Alan ate cabbage sprouts, and mushrooms.		
17. Isaac's shoes were black, red and gold.		
18. Liam and Tom formed a band, although they couldn't play any instruments.		
19. Kellie, shocked at what she read, gave Mark a telling-off.		
20. Rob, smiled lazily.		

Commas, question marks and exclamation marks

Put the question mark or exclamation mark in these sentences in the correct place or places.

21. "Why can't I tie this knot properly " muttered Jim.

22. "Look out " warned Anastasia.

23. "Which of these should I wear " asked Danielle.

24. "Land ahoy. Over there " screamed the ship's watch.

25. "Matthew – why are you asking Amy " said the teacher.

26. "Ow! That hurt " complained Jade.

27. "Is that you, Aaron " asked Adam.

28. "Don't touch that, James " yelled the PE teacher.

29. "Rebecca! Goodness gracious " said her startled sister.

30. "Where is your homework " said the teacher to David.

31. "Brittany! No " raged the team manager.

32. "How did you manage to work that out " asked Steven.

33. "Did your photographs come out OK " remarked Kamal.

34. "Watch my fingers " warned Louis.

35. "You're fired " shouted Bill.

36. "Why am I fired " asked Dean.

37. "Because of all the mistakes you made " retorted Bill, angrily.

38. "Why didn't you sack the others who made mistakes " replied Dean.

39. "Listen to me " screeched Bill.

40. "Why should I listen to someone who shouts all the time " muttered Dean as he left.

/40

Put in the missing apostrophes in these examples.

1. Darren didnt like his new shoes.

2. Samantha wasnt very happy because she had lost her false teeth.

3. Tiffany wasnt late, so the teacher fell over in shock.

4. Anthony couldnt reach the table.

5. April and Chris wouldnt speak to each other.

6. Danielle isnt the smallest in the class, but she looks it.

7. Christian hadnt done his science homework so his teacher was furious.

8. Natasha couldve won the lottery if she had bought a ticket.

9. Jamie shouldve remembered his book but hed flushed it down the loo.

10. Nathan hadnt eaten the pies.

11. "Well go to the pictures to see the new Orlando Bloom film!" said Leanne to Tara.

12. "Cant I come too?" asked an upset Sarah.

13. Chloe and Harriet didnt grumble when the dinner lady gave them meat pie and custard on the same plate.

14. "Im not very quiet..." said Stacey.

15. "Youll make me sick if you do that!" moaned Adam.

16. Jordan shouldve told Jodie that hed taken her pencil case, but he didnt.

17. Sam and Charlotte didnt want to share their dolls with Tom, because he wouldnt give them back.

18. Anoushka didnt like Liam's singing, because he only sang his own songs.

19. Nicole said, "Ill tell my mum, if you pinch my lunch!"

20. Shane and Mark hadnt turned up so they couldnt do the work that had been set.

21. Catherine didnt want to do the work.

22. Mia wouldnt talk in class.

23. "Lauras here!" shouted Rob.

24. Philipa couldnt do the test.

25. "Youre not going out dressed like that."

Fill in the table to indicate whether the apostrophe is in the right place or not. The first one is done for you as an example.

sentence	correct use of apostrophe	incorrect use of apostrophe
Kurt did'nt understand.		✔
26. Joanna baked cookies, but couldn't make trifle.		
27. Tom was'nt watching carefully.		
28. Tara di'dnt get it right.		
29. Elle couldn't understand why her CD player had broken.		
30. Ed shouldn't have plugged the wire into the wrong plug.		
31. "Are'n't you ready yet?"		
32. "Wo'nt you help me?"		
33. "Isn't that the correct answer?"		
34. Andy wished he had'nt boiled his haggis in the old saucepan.		
35. George should've played bass with the band, but the gig was cancelled.		

In these examples, you need to change the words to a shortened version with apostrophes. An example is given to you for the first one.

word	shortened version word	word	shortened version word
can not	can't		
36. should have		37. will not	
38. is not		39. we will	
40. I have		41. you will	
42. they have		43. had not	
44. he had		45. she had	

/45

Speech marks

> Put the speech marks around the direct speech in these examples.

1.   Pass the ball over here, yelled Domenico.

2.   Out! declared the umpire.

3.   Where are my toys? mused Ben.

4.   I think I know the answer, remarked Sam.

5.   That book was amazing, declared Lizzie.

6.   Tony! Come here and see this! shouted Phil, excitedly.

7.   Wait, said Harry, I think I can hear something.

8.   What is it? I hope it's not scary, mumbled Hannah.

9.   Maisie – tuck your shirt in! yelled the teacher.

10. Why don't you borrow Abigail's book? suggested Richard.

> Is the speech punctuation in the right place in relation to the speech marks? The first one is done for you as an example.

speech	correct punctuation	incorrect punctuation
"Which one should I choose"? said Gemma		✔
11. "Don't look at me like that!" joked Frances.		
12. "I'm not going to eat that". said Vicky.		
13. "That'll be £2.25, please," said the dinner lady.		
14. "Can you change a five pound note?" asked the pupil.		
15. "Hygiene is very important. Remember that"! ordered the officer.		
16. "It's true – I've won the lottery!" shrieked Amelia.		
17. "I don't want to grow up," sighed Tom.		
18. "Now where did I put that pen"? mumbled Denise.		
19. "Can we have our ball back, please"? asked the boys.		
20. "Remember to bring a change of clothes," commented the instructor.		

Create some sentences, following the instructions and using speech marks. The first one has been done as an example. There are lots of possible answers.

Example: ....a sentence that uses an exclamation mark.

"Wow!" exclaimed Donna.

21. ...that has a comma before the final speech marks.

_____

22. ...that has a question mark before the final speech marks.

_____

23. ...that uses the word **shouted** after the speech marks.

_____

24. ...that uses a comma and an exclamation mark in the speech.

_____

25. ...that uses the word **sad** in the speech.

_____

26. ...that uses two adjectives in the speech.

_____

27. ...that uses an adverb in the words after the speech.

_____

28. ...that uses a comma, a full-stop and a question mark in the speech.

_____

29. ...that has four words in the speech.

_____

30. ...that uses the adverb **crazily** after the speech.

_____

/30

There, their and they're

Circle the correct version of **there**, **their** or **they're** in each of these.

1. Where were there/their/they're parents when that happened?

2. There/Their/They're is the ball we were looking for!

3. Over there/their/they're is the entrance to the park.

4. There/Their/They're friends were on holiday.

5. There/Their/They're not here today.

6. The girls went to there/their/they're lessons on time.

7. There/Their/They're were no takers for the rock climbing course.

8. There/Their/They're efforts were in vain.

9. There/Their/They're going to the party tonight.

10. There/Their/They're going on there/their/they're holidays next month.

Has the correct version of **there/their/they're** been used in these sentences? Decide whether it has or not. The first one has been done for you as an example.

sentence	correctly used	not correctly used
There are lots of questions to answer.	✔	
11. Their are no right answers.		
12. Their is no proof that the Loch Ness monster exists.		
13. Their holidays were spent looking for the Loch Ness monster.		
14. They wasted there time.		
15. There going to the fair.		
16. Where are their friends?		
17. They're friends were absent.		
18. There is the answer.		
19. They're very brave.		
20. Their coats were muddied.		

There, their and they're

Write 6 sentences using **they're** correctly. There are lots of different answers.

21. _____
22. _____
23. _____
24. _____
25. _____
26. _____

Write 7 sentences using **their** correctly.

27. _____
28. _____
29. _____
30. _____
31. _____
32. _____
33. _____

Write 7 sentences using **there** correctly.

34. _____
35. _____
36. _____
37. _____
38. _____
39. _____
40. _____

/40

More confused words and spellings

In each of these sentences, underline the word that has been used incorrectly.

1. The student excepted the award.

2. The child was adapted by its foster parents.

3. The magician performed an allusion that amazed everyone.

4. Always to the festival were blocked, because of an accident on the motorway.

5. The bare in the zoo looked rather fed up.

6. The landlord got rid of his new border because he wasn't paying his rent.

7. The race coarse was flooded, so the meeting couldn't go ahead.

8. The hard working boy was described as industrial by his teachers.

9. I gave up chocolates for Leant.

10. The morale of the story is that you shouldn't cheat and look at the answers!

In the table below, write the similar sounding words that should have been used in the sentences above.

sentence number	similar sounding word that should have been used
11. 1	
12. 2	
13. 3	
14. 4	
15. 5	
16. 6	
17. 7	
18. 8	
19. 9	
20. 10	

More confused words and spellings

Unscramble these words which are often misspelled. The meanings are there to help you work them out. The first one has been done for you, to give you an example of how the exercise works.

scrambled word	clue	answer
scab nee	the lack of something	absence
21. call ooh	intoxicating drink	
22. panacea per	what something looks like is its...	
23. height	the one after seventh	
24. luau befit	opposite of ugly?	
25. sub en sis	you might set one of these up to make money	
26. rec met ye	a burial ground	
27. comet item	a group of people who talk and make decisions	
28. dearie otter	get worse	
29. freehand hick	something you would use to blow your nose on	
30. a boat lorry	a place where experiments might take place	
31. lie nelsons	what you might feel when you are on your own	
32. aria germ	a ceremony uniting two people	
33. acnes ryes	needed	
34. binge hour	a person who lives next door to you	
35. sure up	to chase after something or someone	
36. cross sis	a tool used to cut things with	
37. cent seen	a group of words that make sense as a unit	
38. ed roils	a member of an army	
39. wired	strange	
40. an villi	a bad guy	

/40

This passage should be split into ten paragraphs.
Mark on where you think each paragraph should start.

The first reason why I love folk music is that it is really easy to make with very few   1
instruments. In the past, people had to make music with whatever they had to hand,
so bones, sticks and stones were early percussion instruments. The next reason why
I like folk music is that it's usually easy to play. Because it was played by ordinary
working people, for their own entertainment, it was not usually complicated, consisting   5
of perhaps only two or three easy chords. That meant that anyone who had a little
knowledge of an instrument could be a folk musician. Thirdly, the stories that are told
in folk music are fascinating. Many of the songs are really just stories with a tune;
classic stories with timeless storylines, of knights, battles, common folk and rich nobles.
Even if you didn't like the music of some of the songs, the stories would fascinate you.   10
A different reason why I like folk music is that it is unfashionable at this moment in time.
Who wants to follow the crowd and be the same as everyone else, mindlessly taking in
what the radio and television says that we are supposed to like? Not me, that's for sure.
In contrast to this, I feel that folk music offers tremendous opportunities to find out
about our past. Many songs have been passed down over hundreds of years and   15
some of the "same" songs exist in slightly different versions all over the country and,
indeed, all over the world. A further reason why I like folk music is that it can be enjoyed
anywhere. It doesn't need expensive microphones and sound equipment (although
they might sometimes help!) and it can be performed in any room, by a small number
of people. Anyone who feels like joining in can add their sound to the music too.   20
My seventh reason is a personal one – there are many performers and singers whose
voices and choice of songs really appeal to me. Whether it is a distinctive female
voice or a mixture of instruments making a certain sound, there are special sounds
that make me feel good when I hear them. Eighth on my list of reasons is the fact that
attending folk music concerts is really cheap! Because the performers don't need   25
expensive stage sets and costumes, this means that ticket prices are kept quite low,
which in turn means that fans like me can attend several concerts at a local venue for
the cost of attending one big show in a massive arena. This leads on to my ninth and
penultimate point. When you are at a folk music concert, you will be close to the
people making the music. You will see their fingers playing the instruments and you   30
will see the glances that the musicians make to each other, the signs that they make
to end the song or to play a solo...and you won't have to look up to see it on a big
video screen. Finally, I realise that folk music is not for everyone, but it does appeal
to all ages and for different reasons – and hopefully will continue to do so, for several
more hundreds, or even thousands, of years!   35

Each paragraph in the passage on page 52 contains a different reason as to why the author likes folk music. Match up the paragraph descriptions with the correct paragraph numbers in the table below.

paragraph	paragraph descriptions
first paragraph	This paragraph talks about why unfashionable folk music is good.
second paragraph	This paragraph talks about how folk music doesn't need expensive equipment.
third paragraph	This paragraph explains why having easy songs is important.
fourth paragraph	This paragraph talks about the cost of attending folk concerts.
fifth paragraph	This paragraph sums up the writer's feelings about folk music.
sixth paragraph	This paragraph talks about how folk music connects us to the past.
seventh paragraph	This paragraph talks about stories in folk music.
eighth paragraph	This paragraph talks about how folk music brings you close to the performers.
ninth paragraph	This paragraph explains why having few instruments is important.
tenth paragraph	This paragraph gives personal reasons for liking folk music.

/10

Words ending in y

All of these verbs end in **y**. Change them to the past tense.

1. reply _____
2. cry _____
3. fortify _____
4. spy _____
5. try _____
6. edify _____
7. clarify _____
8. reply _____
9. dry _____
10. fry _____
11. lay _____
12. pay _____
13. enjoy _____
14. portray _____
15. say _____
16. buy _____
17. pray _____
18. volley _____
19. rely _____
20. carry _____

All of these nouns end in **y**. Change them into plurals.

21. butterfly _____
22. donkey _____
23. journey _____
24. cry _____
25. try _____
26. lady _____
27. day _____
28. puppy _____
29. guy _____
30. city _____
31. toy _____
32. pony _____
33. valley _____
34. company _____
35. play _____
36. turkey _____
37. pantry _____
38. bakery _____
39. quality _____
40. sky _____

Complete this chart. In the chart are a number of words that have been changed from words that ended in **y**. Write the original **y** ending word in the space provided. The first one has been done for you as an example.

word	original ending in y
tried	try
41. stupefied	
42. rectified	
43. babies	
44. beautiful	
45. fryer	
46. heaviness	
47. earliest	
48. trays	
49. mollifies	
50. spied	

Write ten phrases of your own using nouns that end in **y**. There are lots of different answers for this. Don't change the **y** ending into a plural – make sure that it stays as it is.

51. _____   52. _____

53. _____   54 _____.

55. _____   56. _____

57. _____   58. _____

59. _____   60. _____

/60

Words ending in e

The following nouns end in **e**. Change them into the plural form.

1. bone _____

2. hope _____

3. advance _____

4. notice _____

5. absence _____

6. bandage _____

7. battle _____

8. carbohydrate _____

9. stockpile _____

10. pickle _____

The following verbs end in **e**. Change them into nouns.

11. advance _____

12. persuade _____

13. declare _____

14. reduce _____

15. suppose _____

16. acquire _____

17. free _____

18. explore _____

19. exercise _____

20. dispose _____

The following words have been developed from words that end in **e**. Write down the original **e** ending word that they were developed from. The first one has been done for you as an example.

Example: **tabled table**

21. divorced _____

22. drapes _____

23. downsized _____

24. sleaziness _____

25. comparable _____

26. fertiliser _____

27. impurity _____

28. cessation _____

29. capability _____

30. jokingly _____

31. truth   _____

32. wholly   _____

33. clueless   _____

34. courageous   _____

35. noticeable   _____

36. peaceable   _____

37. mated   _____

38. dissuasion   _____

39. duly   _____

40. likeable   _____

Write ten sentences of your own using nouns that end in **e**.
There are lots of different possible answers. Don't change the
ending and make sure the noun keeps its **e** ending unchanged.

41. _____

42. _____

43. _____

44. _____

45. _____

46. _____

47. _____

48. _____

49. _____

50. _____

/50

Reading between the lines

Read the passage below and then read between
the lines to answer the questions which follow.

Photography is a fascinating hobby. In the days before digital cameras, a photographer would
have to be skilled in mixing chemicals and keeping out light so that his negatives weren't ruined.
When photography first started, nobody really knew which chemicals worked best and there were
several different methods that were used to try and get the perfect picture. Substances such as
silver chloride, silver-plated copper and such like were tried with varying degrees of success by
men like Henry Fox Talbot and Louis Daguerre. Because such expensive materials were involved,
photography was still an experimental hobby for the well-off in society, although there was
popular interest in the results.

It wasn't until George Eastman set up the Dry Plate Company in 1880, and produced rolls of film,
that photography's popularity really took off. Photography became cheaper and, in 1900, the
Kodak box roll film camera made it more accessible because of its lower cost and the fact that up
to 100 pictures could be captured on a roll of film.

Experiments in colour photography became more successful in the early part of the 20th century
and many travellers helped to create historical records of the time, although many thought that
they were just taking holiday snaps to show the folks back home!

Photography hasn't always been about preserving a moment in time – ever since photography
started, right up to the present day, there have been people who've sought to deceive the viewer,
either with malicious intent or not. There was a trend in Victorian times to fake ghost pictures and,
later, many governments and individuals realised the power of a carefully constructed image
(especially in wartime) that would tug on people's emotions and get them to change their mind or
opinion. The old adage "the camera never lies" is certainly not true and never has been – it can
quite often lie! It's been made a lot easier since the development of digital cameras and their
phenomenal success. Nowadays, changing photographs has become an art form in itself. There
are still many people who think that images shouldn't be doctored, but should remain as they
were taken. However, they seem to be fighting a losing battle; if you could remove your age lines,
spots and straighten your teeth, you would, wouldn't you?

I certainly would!

1. What does the word "fascinating" suggest about the writer of this passage?
    a) He is interested in photography and wants to get the reader to share his enthusiasm.
    b) He likes using big words.
    c) He likes using descriptive words.
    d) Both a) and b)

2. Why does the writer mention Henry Fox Talbot and Louis Daguerre in the first paragraph?
    a) Because he knows them and wants to show off.
    b) Because he wants to give evidence to show that he knows his subject.
    c) Because they invented digital photography.
    d) Both b) and c)

3. Which phrase in the first paragraph suggests that photography didn't catch on at first?
   a) "nobody really knew"
   b) "varying degrees of success"
   c) "photography was still an experimental hobby"
   d) "Photography is a fascinating hobby."

4. What reasons are suggested in paragraph two for why photography's popularity increased?
   a) Rolls of film were produced.
   b) Photography became cheaper.
   c) A new camera was invented.
   d) All of these.

5. How important is George Eastman to the history of photography, according to paragraph two?
   a) Very
   b) Not at all
   c) A little bit

6. What does the phrase "although many thought that they were just taking holiday snaps" suggest in paragraph three? It suggests that –
   a) The early photographers weren't very good.
   b) The early photographers weren't aware how important their photographs would be.
   c) The early photographers didn't know what they were doing.
   d) Both a) and c)

7. What does the phrase "preserving a moment in time" suggest?
   a) Photographs can make time stand still.
   b) Photographs can save a moment for ever.
   c) Both a) and b)
   d) Photographs are made of chemicals.

8. What main idea does the writer suggest in paragraph four?
   a) That photographs are all unreliable.
   b) That photographs can't always be trusted as a true record of an event.
   c) That photographs cause trouble.

9. Why does the writer use a rhetorical question "you would, wouldn't you?" at the end of paragraph four?
   a) To get the reader to agree with his point of view.
   b) To point out how unreliable photographs are.
   c) To show how photographs might be used.
   d) Both a) and c)

10. Why is the last line in a paragraph of its own?
    a) To add impact.
    b) To show a strong personal opinion.
    c) To trick the reader.
    d) Both a) and b)

/10

Test 1	Test 2	Test 3	Test 4	Test 5
Level 4	Level 4	Level 4	Level 4	Level 4
/50 %	/45 %	/60 %	/30 %	/40 %
Date _____	Date _____	Date _____	Date _____	Date _____

Test 6	Test 7	Test 8	Test 9	Test 10
Level 4	Level 4	Level 4	Did you find all of the words? If you did it in less than 10 minutes, colour this in red, or if you did it in more, colour this in blue.	If you got all of the clues in less than 10 minutes, colour this in red, or colour this in blue if it took you longer.
/40 %	/30 %	/50 %		
Date _____	Date _____	Date _____	Date _____	Date _____

Test 11	Test 12	Test 13	Test 14	Test 15
Level 4	Level 4	Level 4	Level 4	Level 4
/40 %	/60 %	/40 %	/40 %	/40 %
Date _____	Date _____	Date _____	Date _____	Date _____

Test 16	Test 17	Test 18	Test 19	Test 20
Level 4	Level 4	Level 4	Level 4	Did you find all of the words? If you did it in less than 10 minutes, colour this in red, or if you did it in more, colour this in blue.
/45 %	/50 %	/40 %	/30 %	
Date _____	Date _____	Date _____	Date _____	Date _____

Test 21	Test 22	Test 23	Test 24	Test 25
If you got all of the clues in less than 10 minutes, colour this in red, or colour this in blue if it took you longer.	Level 4	Level 4	Level 4	Level 4
	/40 %	/45 %	/30 %	/40 %
Date _____	Date _____	Date _____	Date _____	Date _____

Test 26	Test 27	Test 28	Test 29	Test 30
Level 4	Level 4	Level 4	Level 4	Level 4
/40 %	/10 %	/60 %	/50 %	/10 %
Date _____	Date _____	Date _____	Date _____	Date _____

Colour each box in the correct colour to show how many questions you got right.

0%–20% = yellow, 21%–50% = green, 51%–70% = blue, 71%–100% = red

This will help you to monitor your progress.